P9-BZX-910

Cat & Gnome

Graham Roumieu

ACT 1

We Are So Lonely,

Oh. Hello.

Come here often?

i like your jaunty belt.

Well, I'm off stay cool.

(call me.)

Oh! Hey! How's it going?

I enjoy the Arts Section mostly.

mmtph. Tsk. Tsk.

yaaawn.

uh, I'll see ya.

(days pass)

Hey, listen, about the other...

.... oh, you have company.

I just wanted to invite you to
my party.

It's my birthday next Tuesday.

Uh. You can both come.

(the following Tuesday)

Wow. Awesome turnout,

Have you ever heard the one about the guy with tourettes?

Oh shit Fuck Bitch Cock, it's funny, Monkey Cock!

Bwaaa ha ha ha ha!

What's that? Oh god, sorry dude,
I didn't know your mom
has the Big T.

it is truly the blight of our times
and she is truly a hero.
Bless her heart.

Would it make you feel
any better if I told you it
isn't really my birthday?

This party blows.

There is some time
where nothing much
happens. Maybe, like
two days.

Whatever,

my god! oh my god! oh my god! Oh m.

OHMY GOD! OHMY GOD! OHMY GOD! OHMY GO

OH MY GOD !

I was just up the street
and I saw your snail buddy
get hit by a ice cream truck.

Oh no, I see crows circling.

Don't you die on us Reggie!

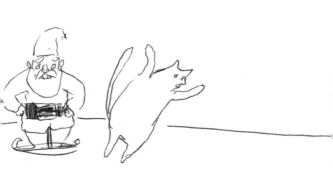

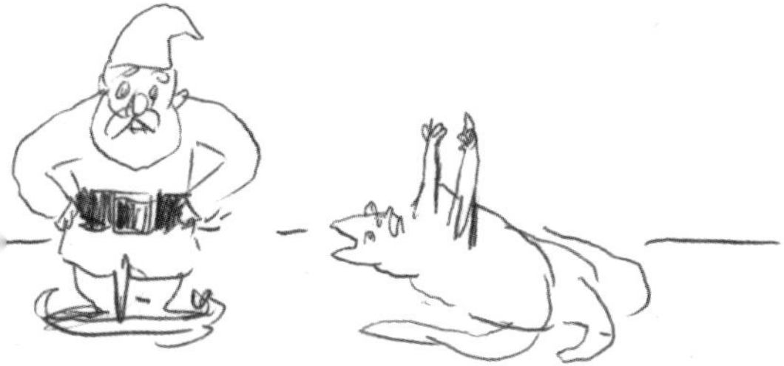

OOOOOOOOOOOOOOOO!

* whimpers * chuffs *

want a slug?

Oh c'mon, lighten up.
Slug,
Snail.
It's funny.

You live by the gun, you die by the gun.

2632

hunngk...

rrgkGHURL!

h... hey. Hey, man.

.... WHAT!

A!

NIGHT!

where is everyone?

HOLY CRAP IT'S THE FUTURE

No wonder that mailbox screamed
"STOP, I AM A CYBERNETIC BEING!"
when I peed on it!

Wait!
No!

Lord. they're all gone!
All my friends are
dead and gone!

And that means nobody
watered my plants,

SURELY MY BEGONIAS ARE FUCKED!

But hey, you're still here.
You waited for me all
these hundreds of years.

Man, and I thought you
didn't even like me.

ehem

uh
wow.
i'm misting up.

Sorry if I sound corny
but its so beautiful
that our friendship
can last even across the
vast expanse of time
and space.

Holy crap are you okay!?

Hey, it's not the
future at all
you assholes,

I hate you!

Boo-hoo. Boo-hoo-hoo-hoo. Boo-hoo...

..Boo-hoo-hoo-bh.. ZZZZZZZZZZZZ

...,Z Z Z Z Z Z z z Z Z z z Z Z z z z z z z z z z,,,

(Some magics happen)

END.

More the end than the last page.

Cast of Stars

Cecil Enrique Ngumbé III is currently seeking employment in the I.T. field.
He is satisfied with his work in this book but wouldn't call it his best.

Mr. Scribbles makes his triumphant return to the paper screen in this the story that will define a generation.
He makes Brando look like a sack of crap.

We had to go with this
guy because that awesome
lobster from the Little
Mermaid was all booked up.
We never even got his name.
Frankly we don't much care. R.I.P.

Denis Witherspoon is a raven,
otherwise known as Corus
Corax which are considered
amongst the smartest of birds.
If he craps on you, it was
no accident,

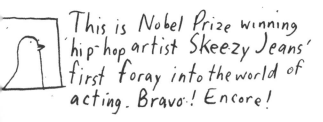

This is Nobel Prize winning
hip-hop artist Skeezy Jeans'
first foray into the world of
acting. Bravo! Encore!